KV-702-165

ESKENAZI

ESKENAZI

Seven classical Chinese paintings

29 October - 27 November 2009

10 Clifford Street
London W1S 2LJ
Telephone: 020 7493 5464
Fax: 020 7499 3136
e-mail: gallery@eskenazi.co.uk
web: www.eskenazi.co.uk

ISBN: 1 873609 27 2

Designed and typeset by Daniel M Eskenazi, London
Photography by Mike Bruce, London
Printed and originated by The Colour House, London

Foreword

I purchased all the paintings in this exhibition, apart from one, between 1984 and 1990. I was prompted to look seriously at early Chinese paintings in the 1970's, after meeting John M. Crawford and C.C. Wang in New York who kindly invited me to study their two great collections. C.C., in particular, as a famous practising artist as well as a connoisseur of earlier paintings, was an enormous influence. However, it was not until I started discussing classical paintings with Arnold Chang that I had the courage to make my first purchase. Arnold at the time was the recently appointed head of the new department of Chinese paintings at Sotheby's in New York. Both then and later he could not have been more encouraging or more generous with his objective advice.

I spent more and more time looking at paintings – in Taiwan, Japan and the U.S.A., all countries with repositories of masterpieces. I also started to read up on the subject and soon realized it was not without pitfalls, especially regarding attribution and dating. Subjective feeling had to be combined with objective connoisseurship and these are the criteria that led to my acquisition of the works you will see in this catalogue. I was much heartened when I showed them to the late Dr. Sherman Lee, another important mentor to me as well as a true friend. 'I don't know about the artists but you have a group of very fine early paintings', he said, and I could not have been happier.

I would particularly like to thank Roderick Whitfield, Percival David Emeritus Professor of Chinese & East Asian Art, School of Oriental & African Studies, University of London, an eminent authority on Chinese paintings, for his detailed and informative introduction to this catalogue. The reader, whether visiting the exhibition or not (I hope the former), will be rewarded by a greater understanding of the particular qualities of these paintings as well as the context within which they were created.

Philip Constantinidi has written the catalogue entries and footnotes for which I am most grateful, especially since he was navigating in unfamiliar waters. I would like to thank Yuansheng Wang who has written the Chinese captions and proved inexhaustible in tracking down and interpreting the obscurest seal, Laura Eskenazi for her diligent proof-reading of both the English and the Chinese texts, and Mike Bruce for his sensitive photography.

Giuseppe Eskenazi

Chronology
Chinese Dynasties and Periods

		BC 公元前	AD 公元
Xia period	夏	2100c – 1600c	
Period of Erlitou culture	二里头文化	1900 – 1600	
Shang period	商	1600c – 1027	
Zhengzhou phase	郑州阶段	1600 – 1400	
Anyang phase	安阳阶段	1300 – 1027	
Zhou period	周	1027 – 256	
Western Zhou	西周	1027 – 771	
Eastern Zhou	东周	770 – 256	
Spring and Autumn period	春秋	770 – 476	
Warring States period	战国	475 – 221	
Qin dynasty	秦	221 – 206	
Han dynasty	汉	206 –	220
Western Han	西汉	206 –	9
Xin dynasty (Wang Mang)	新（王莽）		9 – 23
Eastern Han	东汉		25 – 220
Six Dynasties period	六朝		220 – 581
Three Kingdoms	三国		220 – 280
Western Jin	西晋		265 – 317
Eastern Jin	东晋		317 – 420
Liu Song	刘宋		420 – 479
Southern Qi	南齐		479 – 502
Liang	梁		502 – 557
Chen	陈		557 – 589
Sixteen Kingdoms	十六国		304 – 439
Northern Wei	北魏		386 – 535
Western Wei	西魏		535 – 557
Eastern Wei	东魏		534 – 549
Northern Qi	北齐		550 – 577
Northern Zhou	北周		557 – 581
Sui dynasty	隋		581 – 618
Tang dynasty	唐		618 – 907
Five dynasties	五代		907 – 960
Liao dynasty	辽		907 –1125
Song dynasty	宋		960 –1279
Northern	北宋		960 –1127
Southern	南宋		1127 –1279
Jin dynasty	金		1115 –1234

		BC 公元前	AD 公元
Yuan dynasty	元		1279 –1368
Ming dynasty	明		1368 –1644
Hongwu	洪武		1368 –1398
Jianwen	建文		1399 –1402
Yongle	永乐		1403 –1424
Hongxi	洪熙		1425
Xuande	宣德		1426 –1435
Zhengtong	正统		1436 –1449
Jingtai	景泰		1450 –1456
Tianshun	天顺		1457 –1464
Chenghua	成化		1465 –1487
Hongzhi	弘治		1488 –1505
Zhengde	正德		1506 –1521
Jiajing	嘉靖		1522 –1566
Longqing	隆庆		1567 –1572
Wanli	万历		1573 –1619
Taichang	泰昌		1620
Tianqi	天启		1621 –1627
Chongzheng	崇祯		1628 –1644
Qing dynasty	清		1644 –1911
Shunzhi	顺治		1644 –1661
Kangxi	康熙		1662 –1722
Yongzheng	雍正		1723 –1735
Qianlong	乾隆		1736 –1795
Jiaqing	嘉庆		1796 –1820
Daoguang	道光		1821 –1850
Xianfeng	咸丰		1851 –1861
Tongzhi	同治		1862 –1874
Guangxu	光绪		1875 –1908
Xuantong	宣统		1909 –1911
Republic of China	中华民国		1911 –1949
People's Republic of China	中华人民共和国		1949

Fig. 1
Traditionally attributed to Hu Gui, Chinese, first half of 10th century
Khitan Falconer with Horse
Chinese, Southern Song dynasty, 12th century
Ink, colour, and gold on silk
23.4 x 24.1 cm (9 3/16 x 9 1/2 in)
Museum of Fine Arts, Boston
Special Chinese and Japanese Fund, 12.895

Introduction
by **Roderick Whitfield**

From the earliest times, Chinese connoisseurs have valued the art of painting for its ability to transcend the limitations of space and time, and to portray exemplars of outstanding quality, uplifting the spirits of those who viewed them. Thus Zong Bing, writing in the first half of the fifth century AD, noted how immense landscapes could be compressed within a small compass: "the form of K'un-lun's Lang peak can be encompassed in a square inch."[1] It might be said that this property lay in the very nature of silk, which was so responsive to the touch of slender brushes, and which, because of the sheer density and number of threads, was necessarily woven on a fairly narrow loom. Handscrolls, no matter how long, could still be no more than a foot or so in height, and album leaves no more than a foot square, challenging the artist to display consummate skill with brush and ink. So it is with the present selection: though small in scale and limited in number, each of these paintings has a powerful resonance with Chinese understanding of nature and of their own history.

Falconer and Horse, catalogue number 1

To take the first of them as an example, we see a fine steed, saddled and with a tiger-skin saddle-cloth, closely attended by a groom, who carries a peregrine falcon (probably a female, larger and heavier than the male, which is properly known as a tercel) on his gloved right hand. Peregrine falcons are the swiftest animals on earth, employed in hunting for millennia by the nomads of Central Asia. Similar tiger-skin and leopard-skin saddle-cloths are seen in a pair of small paintings in the collection of the National Palace Museum, Taipei, since mounted as tall hanging scrolls, by the tenth-century painter Hu Gui. On the one, *Going Out on the Hunt*, three of the four riders carry peregrine falcons, the fourth a magnificent eagle; the other, *Returning from the Hunt*, shows three attendants, each carrying a greyhound on or behind the saddle.[2] All seven riders are identifiable by their close-shaven heads, leaving just a wisp of hair on either side, as being of Khitan or Liao nationality.

Indeed, the close-fitting cap, tunic and trousers worn by the groom in the Eskenazi painting, as well as his neat beard and moustaches, suggest that he is from Central Asia, while the featureless background, common to such paintings, portrays the vast expanses of the steppes, here broken only by the lightly inscribed signature of the Southern Song artist Chen Juzhong (active early 13th century), an artist known for his imitations of Liao paintings.[3] The painter has paid minute attention to every detail of the horse's appearance and behaviour. Though its mane is not plaited or crenellated, the tail is tied in a knot with two loose ends, in a fashion that has been traced back through Tang examples to Sasanian Iran.[4] The horse waits calmly, saddled and obedient, without any need for the groom to hold the bridle or use the whip that is barely discernible behind his back.

The question of whether the horse and the falcon in this painting have more of the character of tribute brought to China, or whether they represent Khitan lifestyle as in the case of Hu Gui's paintings in the National Palace Museum, may be resolved by comparison with another painting attributed to Hu Gui, in the collection of the Museum of Fine Arts, Boston, which appears close in character to the present album leaf,[5] (figure 1). Although recently re-attributed to the Southern Song dynasty by Wu Tung, the authentic characterization of the subject in the Boston fan surely supports its claim to date from Hu Gui's time. It refers to the swan hunts that were a regular spring and autumn tradition of the Khitans. The rider in the Boston painting wears a similar close-fitting cap and a long riding coat (apparently embroidered in gold on the back, shoulders and collar). He has a knife or short sword tucked into the belt, as he secures a splendid swan behind the saddle. A falcon, no doubt the *haidongqing,* lammergeier or gyrfalcon (Falco rusticolus), prized since Tang times, but especially in Liao and Jin for its swan-hunting prowess, perches high on the pommel, watching with interest. The saddle-cloth here has the same shape, generously covering the forequarters, as the tiger-skin saddle-cloth in the album leaf, but is decorated, again probably in embroidery, with a magnificent pair of swans in flight. We can imagine that the part hidden behind the rider also depicted a falcon in a steep dive towards them.[6] The horse, somewhat restively moving forward to graze on the scanty grass, is black with white blaze and lower legs, has gilded halter and harness straps and its tail is tied up in a similar double end.

The motif of a sable horse with white fetlocks and a white blaze is seen throughout many centuries. One example is even ascribed, by no less an authority than Emperor Huizong, to the famous Tang horse painter Han Gan.[7] More convincing is the record of one of the warhorses ridden by Li Shimin (who reigned as Taizong from 624 to 649) in the founding year of the Tang dynasty, 618. The occasion took place during Li's campaign against the rebel leader Xue Renguo, and is commemorated in one of the large bas-reliefs at the northern gate of Taizong's tomb, Zhaoling, probably after a painting by the court figure painter Yan Liben (d. 673). The relief, long since removed to the Beilin Museum, Xi'an, Shaanxi, shows the horse at full gallop, recalling the occasion when Taizong rode it for two hundred *li* in a single night. The horse's name was Baidiwu 白蹄乌, or White-footed Crow, and was celebrated in the poem accompanying the relief:

'With a sword long enough to touch the sky,
This swift steed could run with the wind;
At a gallop I pacified Long,
Turning in the saddle I settled Shu'.[8]

Throughout history, fine horses were brought as tribute to China. A handscroll by the Northern Song master Li Gonglin[9], sadly lost since the early twentieth century, showed five splendid steeds, each accompanied by a foreign groom. An album leaf on paper by the Yuan master Zhao Mengfu (1254 - 1322), in the National Palace Museum, shows such a horse with four white fetlocks, mane blowing in the wind, and groom,[10] while his contemporary Liu Guandao (active mid-14th century) depicted the Yuan emperor Qubilai Khan on a hunt, riding a black horse with the same white blaze and fetlocks.[11] The appearance on the Eskenazi painting of the seal of a Ming imperial prince, Zhu Gang, an older brother of the great Yongle emperor Zhu Di, is vivid evidence of the continued interest of the Ming aristocracy in fine horses. Consciously or not, therefore, the subject of a non-Chinese groom leading a fine horse refers to the vast extent of the Chinese empire and its tributary relations, as well as to the equestrian and hunting life of China's northern neighbours.

Landscape, catalogue number 2

Though similar in size and in tonality, this landscape carries a quite different and less confident message. The work of an anonymous painter of the Southern Song, it must surely allude to the situation of China at the time. Although the landscape of low hills and waterways is like that near Hangzhou to which the Song court had retreated in 1139, some years after the Jin defeat of the Northern Song, the scene is of a desolate wintry day, with a leaden sky and snow lying on the ground. On a bank near the foreground, a gaggle of geese crane their necks towards a flock of crows flying into the distance. The atmosphere seems heavy with nostalgia for the loss of north China to the Jin Tartars, and a longing to return.

The sombre atmosphere is not unlike that evoked in two square album leaves of similar size to this leaf, depicting landscapes with travellers in ox-carts, both in the Shanghai Museum.[12] In the one, signed by the Southern Song painter Zhu Rui (active ca. 1131 - 62), one cart, drawn by three oxen and with a dog sitting on the back platform, watching his master who follows on a donkey, is fording a river, while another disappears into the mists up a track overshadowed by leafless trees; the other, signed Zhu with an illegible given name, has three ox-carts, their woven wicker roofs topped with snow (and in one case a table strapped on upside down), negotiating a hazardous track through the marshes and over a steep bridge into the distance, where a fourth ox-cart is seen fording the river. The travellers seem to be refugees; danger seems to lurk at every turn, with steep edges to the road and menacing rocks in the water. Clumps of evergreen trees, like the clump in the Eskenazi leaf, top the low hills in the far distance.

Scenes of ox-carts in wintry landscapes had been a favourite theme of painters in the eleventh century, where they characterized both the rugged mountainous landscapes of north China and the prosperity of the Northern Song dynasty. In contrast, the present leaf and the two leaves in Shanghai show no truly lofty mountain peaks, no roadside inns with resting travellers and their beasts, and no remote and tranquil monasteries, only a chill descending on the pleasant watery landscape of the lower Yangtze region. This is a variation on the famous 'one-corner' compositions of the Southern Song academy: the anonymous painter displays an extraordinary command of graded ink-wash in the seamless depiction of water, banks and slopes, with fine distinctions between the reed beds at the water's edge and the low-growing bamboo beneath the foreground tree, while the crows in flight help to suggest a vast airy space in the middle distance.

Pavilion of Prince Teng, catalogue number 5

A totally different atmosphere, as well as the sheer inventiveness of Chinese painting, is admirably displayed in the short handscroll composition entitled *Pavilion of Prince Teng*. The viewer is immediately amazed by the intricacy of the architecture and the incredible miniaturization of the inscription, in which the painter has transcribed the whole of a poem by the Tang poet Wang Bo, who composed it as a young man when visiting the Pavilion in 675.[13] The Pavilion itself, an architectural marvel overlooking the Gan River in Nanchang, Jiangxi Province, had been built some twenty-odd years earlier by Li Yuanying, son of the first Tang emperor, in 653. In some nine hundred characters Wang Bo describes the scene and the occasion, in late autumn, with myriad allusions to the splendour of the setting and the nobility of his host, and reflects on the inevitable transience of human life, ending with a poem whose last couplet asks:

'The pavilion's prince –
Where is he now?
Beyond the railing, the lengthy river
flows by in vain'.[14]

While Wang Bo's preface became as famous as the pavilion that it describes, the painter Wang Zhenpeng (active early to mid-14th century), whose signature appears at the end of the inscription, achieved an equal renown as the pioneer of a distinctive style of architectural painting at the Mongol court under Emperor Renzong (r.1312 - 1320).[15] The Yuan writer Yu Ji (1272 - 1348) wrote his father's epitaph, from which we learn that Wang Zhenpeng was at one time "Registrar of the Imperial Library, where he was able to examine all the ancient paintings in its inventory. As a result, his knowledge in painting was greatly advanced."[16] Yu Ji also recorded, in a colophon to Wang Zhenpeng's painting (now lost) of the *Da An Ge* (*Pavilion of Great Peace*) at the Mongols' northern capital, Shangdu, that Qubilai Khan used timbers removed from the Xichun Pavilion of the former Song capital at Bianjing (modern Kaifeng in Henan Province) for the construction of the *Da An Ge*.[17] In deference to the nomad traditions of the grasslands, the layout of this and the many other splendid buildings of Shangdu did not need to obey the traditional Chinese principle of axial symmetry.

Wang Zhenpeng's fine style, matching the Tang verses in very small regular script with detailed though imaginary depictions of famous buildings of the past and elaborate pageantry such as the *Dragon-Boat Regatta on the Jinming Lake*, dated 1323, now in the Metropolitan Museum of Art,[18] was perfectly suited to the ambitions of the Mongol aristocracy. Wang's style was quickly adopted by his followers, notably Xia Yong (active mid-14th century). Among his paintings of similar subjects, Xia Yong's fan depicting the *Yueyang Tower*, dated 1347, in the Palace Museum, Peking, is only 24.7cm across, with the inscription of almost four hundred characters crammed into a space no more than 3cm high and 7cm across;[19] his other paintings are all around 25 or 26cm square, with similar densely-packed inscriptions. Besides the *Yueyang Tower* and the *Yellow Crane Tower,*[20] Xia Yong also depicted the *Pavilion of Prince Teng* several times, in square album leaves, omitting some of the buildings and drastically compressing the rest, though retaining the general aspect and the single sail on the river. Examples are in the Freer Gallery of Art, the Museum of Fine Arts, Boston[21] (figure 2), the Shanghai Museum and the Palace Museum, Peking.

Comparing these tightly organized versions by Xia Yong and their miniaturized inscriptions with surviving paintings by Wang Zhenpeng, Xia Yong's indebtedness to his older contemporary and his own limitations are clear. In a variation on the "one-corner" landscape compositions favoured by Ma Yuan and his followers at the Southern Song court, Xia Yong places the principal buildings on the right or left, according to the subject, and reduces the distant landscape so that it can fit beneath the inscription block. In the case of the *Pavilion of Prince Teng* he emphasizes the dizzying height of the buildings, setting them on a brick platform with sheer near-vertical walls. Wang Zhenpeng's compositions, on the other hand, are not confined to a square foot of silk, and as well as architectural subjects and the panoply of the *Dragon-Boat Regatta,* he also painted large figures, as in the handscroll of *The Hermit Boya Playing the Qin for his Friend Zhong Qiqi*, in the Palace Museum, Peking.[22] In the case of the Eskenazi handscroll, it would appear that a section of the composition is missing at the beginning, so that the work could have originally been at least half as long again as the present length of 71cm. As with Wang's *Dragon-Boat Regatta on the Jinming Lake,* the water of the Gan River is simply depicted as empty space, with a single sailboat near the end of the composition. A massive peak looms out of the mists that merge imperceptibly with the river: more distant summits lead the eye to the inscription, which measures some 7 by 10cm, close to four times the area of Xia Yong's feats of miniaturization. It has to be said, however, that the writing itself is less disciplined than that of either Wang or Xia: the characters do not keep to a strictly vertical column, as is required for writing in *xiaokai*, small regular script.

The architecture displays great variety and is eminently accessible to the viewer, in the same way that Chen Yunru in her article (note 15, below) has characterized Wang Zhenpeng's depiction of the spaces in *Dragon-Boat Regatta.* There are stairways and entrances, an enclosed courtyard, and in addition to the imposing three-storey main building, a fine square pavilion with the cross-shaped four-gable roof that was introduced in the Yuan dynasty. The National Palace Museum in Taipei has a large hanging scroll, *The Han Palace,* by Wang Zhenpeng's fourteenth-century disciple Li Rongjin, which Anita Chung has described as ". . . a superb example of Yuan *jiehua.* The careful arrangement of the architectural forms builds up a monumental compound punctuated rhythmically with open spaces, height variations, and natural elements. Numerous fine-line details and repetitive surface patterns add to the finesse of the architectural images."[23] *Mutatis mutandis*, since *The Han Palace* is not a handscroll, her words could equally well apply to the painting exhibited here. Taken with the evident age of the silk with its numerous repairs along the upper edge, these features of the painting are a definite encouragement to consider it as a near-contemporary copy of an original composition by Wang Zhenpeng, or the work of one of his followers.

Girls gathering foxnuts, catalogue number 3

Anonymous, *Gathering Qian*, (formerly attributed to Zhao Mengfu, 1254 - 1322).
The inscription on the facing page, in his familiar style based on the graceful calligraphy of Yun Shouping (1633 - 1690), is by the Qing painter Fei Danxu (1801 - 1850):

> 'Six hundred autumns have passed since the master's[24] birth,
> Yet open the picture and feel the former wind once more.
> Outside Gull Wave Pavilion, a flawless spring,
> Are the girls from Wu still gathering foxnuts?

Fig. 2
Xia Yong, Chinese, 1340s - 1360s
The Palace of Prince Teng
Chinese, Yuan dynasty, mid 14th century
Ink on silk
24.7 x 24.7cm (9 3/4 x 9 3/4 in)
Museum of Fine Arts, Boston

> Wenmin's paintings have never been surpassed. I am fortunate to have been born in this district, where the memory and enduring fragrance of his style still flows good and plenty. In the winter of *wushen* (1848) when I was living at Dixi, Master Zhang Zibo showed me this leaf of *Gathering Qian* in his collection. Having gazed at the scene and admired the famed composition, suddenly it was as though I had been transported to Gull Wave Pavilion.[25] Alas! this site has long gone to waste, and its mist and waves have become a major thoroughfare for boats. Now nobody who lives there grows *qian*. So I have composed a poem about it. Although one may say that it is a figure of the imagination, one might also regard it as a record of actuality.
>
> Respectfully inscribed by [Zhao's] follower Fei Danxu in the 28th year of Daoguang (1848), three days before Changzhi (the winter solstice)'.

The painting bears a seal reading *Zhaoshi Zi'ang* in the lower right corner, similar to but not actually a recorded example of one of Zhao Mengfu's commonly-used seals. Fei Danxu clearly admired and regarded the painting as being an original work by Wenmin, i.e. Zhao Mengfu, but this is most unlikely. The seal in the lower left corner, reading *Zhangshi Zibo guomu* "Zhang Zibo viewed," is that of the painter and calligrapher Zhang Shouxian (1804 - 1875), referred to in the colophon as Zhang Zibo.

Fei's colophon tells us that in his day the site of Zhao Mengfu's pavilion had been overtaken by commercial activities, so that one could no longer observe the peaceful scene depicted in the painting, namely the gathering of *qian* or *qianshi,* the foxnut or Gorgon plant*,* also known as *jitou*, Rooster Head, a kind of waterlily similar to the giant Amazonian lily *Victoria Regia*. One can perhaps see why when we read a verse by the Northern Song poet, Mei Yaochen (1002 - 1060), entitled like this album leaf, *Gathering Qian:*

> 'Their green hedgehog spines are cruel even when torn,
> Like bronze dishes with straight sides, the nails stick up.
> Those rooster heads from Wu:[26] split their deep red caps,
> And pluck bright real pearls out of their oysters.
> Grind them to powder, rinse the slippery white peel,
> Break the skins and boil them in the pot with a sound of wind and waves.
> With row on row of cowrie teeth they put the bright moon to shame,
> No more will Manqing's stomach rumble.
> No matter whether a bushel is dear or cheap,
> There will be no more bad characters at court'.

The floating leaves are circular, with upright edges, and as the Latin name, *ferox,* implies, covered with aggressive spines. The fruits are dark red, hence the name Rooster Head (or Cock's Comb), and contain pearl-like seeds, which are ground into flour. The hungry Manqing is the childhood name of the Han Daoist Dongfang Shuo (154 - 93 BC) who at the age of three is said to have stolen the peaches of longevity from the Queen Mother of the West.[27] Perhaps the *qian* fruits, once prepared, were equally delicious? Numerous fruits can be seen piled up in the boat, but one feels sorry for the girls who have to brave the spines to retrieve them from the waters of the lake. Their foreheads are painted white like those of Song court ladies, and their physique still recalls the ladies of late Tang. Whether the painting itself is Southern Song or Yuan in date is hard to determine, but the whole scene of the shallow pond, willows blowing in the spring breeze, and the anticipation of a culinary treat to reward the girls' hard work, show the painter's talent to arouse all of the senses through the medium of brush and ink and subtle colours.

Melon and grasses, catalogue number 7

Another work, the album leaf of a *Melon Vine*, bears no signature or seal of the artist, yet invites us to believe that it might date from the early Yuan and perhaps even be associated with a particular painter. Alone among this small group of paintings, it is depicted on paper instead of on silk. The smooth texture of the paper is typical of its time, and the delicate execution bears considerable resemblance to paintings on paper by or attributed to the late Southern Song master Qian Xuan (ca.1235 - after 1300), particularly the handscroll *Early Autumn*, in the Detroit Institute of Arts.[28] While a fresh vine stem with bud and flower and tendrils climbs up in one direction, the older leaves and the underside of the melon are discoloured where they touch the ground, like the decaying edges of the great lotus leaf in the Detroit scroll.[29] The four-part seed heads of the grasses,[30] too, look remarkably similar in both paintings, with small touches of the brush to depict their spiky racemes. A similar grass is seen in the album leaf, *Melon and Katydids*, in the National Palace Museum, by Han You (active at the Southern Song court academy in the Shaoxing reign, 1131 - 62).[31]

Qian Xuan would have been too subtle an artist to reveal directly the hidden meaning of his subject, but Lü Jingfu who took the same subject in a painting now in the Nezu Museum of Fine Art, Tokyo,[32] added a verse that helps to explain its poignancy in paintings executed while China was under Mongol rule:

> 'The spirit of the brush raises with a sigh the ghost of Shao Ping;
> Without great concentration, no wonders will be spoken.
> I'm afraid that with only a foot or so of Yanteng paper,[33]
> How possibly can one reach the old green gate'?[34]

Shao Ping lived in the Western Han dynasty and raised melons by the eastern gate of the capital Chang'an; in the Wang Mang interregnum (8 - 23 AD) there was a massacre of some 3000 men near that gate. In this way, melons became a symbol of loyalty for men like Qian Xuan who were born and educated under the Song dynasty and then had to survive under the Mongols. Melon vines are commonly seen among the motifs on blue and white dishes of the mid-fourteenth century: one wonders if these too were mute protests against Mongol rule.

Despite all these indications that point to a Yuan origin for this leaf, however, some doubts must remain. The catalogue description has already referred to the hanging scroll with a very similar but mirror-reversed composition in the National Palace Museum, inscribed at the top of the painting by Qian Xuan himself.[35] Appropriately, this work has a complete set of the standard five imperial seals of the Qianlong Imperial collection. The leaf on exhibition here has two of Qianlong's seals, one at the top centre and the other near the top of the left edge, with about half of each seal visible. Six seals of the Ming collector Xiang Yuanbian (1525 - 1590) also appear, three on each side. In the lower right corner, a single character is all that remains of a seal of the foremost Ming literatus painter, Shen Zhou (1427 - 1509).[36] The impressions of the Xiang seals in particular appear rather worn, with thickened strokes and missing borders. Moreover, while the composition as a whole, as well as the outline of each leaf, is a mirror-reversal of the painting in the National Palace Museum, so that one is clearly copied from the other, there are differences in the grass stems, which are shortened to fit into the album leaf space, and particularly in the tendrils that curl around them. In the hanging scroll, there are three tendrils, all near the tip of the advancing melon stem. They spring from the main stem at the base of a leaf or flower bud. Two have already anchored themselves to grass stems in a series of loops, while the tip of each tapers away to near-invisibility in a short and close-set spiral; the third, that has yet to find a stem to grasp, has a gentle S-shape and has no loops or spirals. In the album leaf, on the other hand, the tendrils are purely decorative. It is impossible to determine where they spring from, since in each case the base of the tendril is hidden behind a leaf, flower, or the melon fruit itself. The spirals do not embrace the grass stems with delicate accuracy, but seem to be calligraphically conceived, and the tips of each tendril widen and in some cases darken, rather than tapering into near-invisibility. Despite their closeness in terms of composition and colouring technique, therefore, one has to conclude that the two works are by different hands. Most likely, the album leaf is a tracing copy; yet the Shen Zhou seal, as well as the character of the paper surface, and the presence of some repairs, for instance in the open flower and the adjacent stem, combine to take its history back to the early Ming dynasty, and possibly beyond.

An old man resting under a pine trees, catalogue number 4

The noted collector C. C. Wang believed that the painting could be by the Yuan artist Sheng Mao (active circa 1295 - 1368). Indeed the subject-matter is close to that seen in a number of his paintings, including fan paintings in various museums, in which a solitary figure, or a pair of figures are seen seated in a landscape beneath trees. Despite these similarities, it must be pointed out that in all of Sheng Mao's paintings, whether fans or hanging scrolls, there is a view of distant hills. Here, the indication of banks and a stream behind the trees offers no further depth of field, in an arrangement more often seen in the Ming dynasty.

It should be noted, moreover, that the fan shape of Sheng Mao's day was not a perfect circle, but an oblong with rounded corners, almost a centimetre wider than tall, and typically although not invariably with a slight concavity at the centre of the lower edge, where the frame met the central rib, when the fan served a practical purpose. The painting of *Ducks in a Lotus Pond* in this exhibition (catalogue number 6) is an example of this traditional fan shape; truly circular fans were to become popular much later, in the Qing dynasty. The present painting, which has been cut to an almost exact circle, was never mounted as a fan. The way in which the trees are cut off, particularly in the upper left segment, suggests that it was originally a rectangular or square album leaf.

Ducks in a lotus pond, catalogue number 6

This painting has the classical fan shape, though there is no sign of a central rib. It is a variation of the theme explored by the Southern Song artist Feng Dayou in his delightful *Lotus and Mandarin Ducks* in the National Palace Museum, (figure 3). Feng Dayou's composition takes the viewer down to the water level, showing the ducks dabbling under, around and behind the lotus leaves, with duckweed covering the water surface. In the present composition, the ducks are all swimming to the left against a sweeping current, while the leaves are blown to the right. The contrast in green tones between the underside and top of the leaves, often exploited in such decorative paintings, makes prominent patches of emerald green, whose shapes are echoed in monochrome in the background, that can be seen either as more lotus leaves or perhaps as the outines of distant hills. The lively attitudes and colouring of the ducks have antecedents in the art of the Northern Song artist Zhao Lingrang, for example in his painting of *Summer Mist along the Lake Shore*, dated 1100, in the Museum of Fine Arts, Boston. The theme of ducks and lotus, however, continued to be popular throughout the Southern Song and Yuan dynasties.[37] In the Yuan dynasty, the well-known connoisseur and painter Ke Jiusi (1290 - 1343) recorded that: "in the Tianli reign (1329 - 1330) most of the imperial robes [were embroidered with] small scenes of ponds; these were called *manchijiao*, 'Loveliness Fills the Pond.'" His poem takes the same title:

> 'Look at the lotus pool with its expanse of flowers and stems
> Pairs of gaily-coloured ducks play among the reds and greens.
> Tell that young girl to take good notc
> And embroider the imperial shirt with all the loveliness of the pond'.[38]

Fig. 3
Feng Dayou, Chinese, c. 12th century
Lotus and Mandarin Ducks
Ink and colour on silk
23.8 x 25.1cm (9 2/5 x 9 9/10in)
National Palace Museum, Taibei

Notes

[1]Susan Bush and Hsio-yen Shih, ed., *Early Chinese Texts on Painting,* Cambridge, Mass.: Harvard University Press, 1985, p.37.

[2]See Lin Boting, ed., *Grand View: Special Exhibition of Northern Sung Painting and Calligraphy.* Taipei: National Palace Museum, 2006, pp.267 - 269, nos. 44 - 45 (01289-6, 01291-2).

[3]Wu Tung, *Masterpieces of Chinese Painting from the Museum of Fine Arts, Boston: Tang through Yuan Dynasties*. Tokyo: Otsuka Kogeisha, 1996, plates volume, pl.25; text volume, p.42; also Wu Tung, *Tales from the Land of Dragons: 1000 Years of Chinese Painting*, Boston: Museum of Fine Arts, 1997, no.16, p.145.

[4]See the detailed review of horses' tails undertaken by Zhou Xiuqin in her comprehensive study: "Zhaoling: The Mausoleum of Emperor Tang Taizong" *Sino-Platonic Papers* no. 187 (April, 2009), chapter 5.

[5]Wu Tung, *Masterpieces*, plates volume, pl.25; text volume, p.42; *Tales from the Land of Dragons*, no.16, p.145.

[6]On the spring and autumn swan hunts of the Jin Khitans and their depiction in brocades and other media, see James C. Y. Watt and Anne E. Wardwell, *When Silk Was Gold: Central Asian and Chinese Textiles,* New York: The Metropolitan Museum of Art, 1997, pp.107 - 8.

[7]*National Palace Museum, Special Exhibition of Horse Paintings,* 1996, pl.1, p.7.

[8]Translation adapted from Zhou Xiuqin, op. cit., p.111.

[9]Robert Harrist, *Power and Virtue: The Horse in Chinese Art,* New York: China Institute, 1997, p.27, Fig.7.

[10]*National Palace Museum, Special Exhibition of Horse Paintings,* 1996, pl.21, p.33.

[11]*National Palace Museum, Special Exhibition of Horse Paintings,* 1996, pl.20, pp.29 - 32.

[12]*Illustrated Catalogue of Selected Works of Ancient Chinese Painting and Calligraphy,* 1987 vol.2, *Collections of the Shanghai Museum*, 1-0044, 1-0043.

[13]See Richard E. Strassberg, *Inscribed Landscapes: Travel Writing from Imperial China.* Berkeley and Los Angeles: University of California Press, 1994, pp.105 - 109.

[14]Translated by Richard E. Strassberg, *ibid.* p.109.

[15]See the extensive review of Wang Zhenpeng's *jiehua* or "ruled line painting" by Chen Yunru, "*Jiehua* zai Song Yuan shiqi de zhuanxi: yi Wang Zhenpeng de *jiehua* weilie" (The development of 'ruled-line painting' in the Song and Yuan period as seen through Wang Zhenpeng's 'ruled-line painting' *Meishushi yanjiu jikan*, vol.26, Taipei: National Taiwan University, 2009, pp.135 - 192.

[16]Quoted from Wai-kam Ho's translation of the epitaph in Sherman E. Lee and Wai-kam Ho, *Chinese Art under the Mongols, 1279 - 1368,* Cleveland: Cleveland Museum of Art, 1968, no.201.

[17]Chen Yunru, *op.cit.*, p.160.

[18]Lee and Ho, *op.cit.* The artist's inscription in well-spaced *lishu* (clerical script) states that the painting was made at the request of the Grand Elder Princess, repeating an earlier version presented to Renzong in 1310 when he was still Heir Apparent. Perhaps the earlier painting is the one of which a section still survives in the National Palace Museum, see the colour plate in Chen Yunru, *op.cit.* In his entry in *Chinese Art under the Mongols,* Wai-kam Ho noted a total of six extant versions in all of the *Dragon-Boat Regatta*.

[19]*Zhongguo gudai shuhua tumu,* vol.19, Jing 1-800.

[20]Yunnan Provincial Museum, see *Zhongguo gudai shuhua tumu, Illustrated Catalogue of Selected Works of Chinese Painting and Calligraphy,* Beijing: Wenwu Press, 1998, vol. 18, Dian 4-05.

[21]Wu Tung, *Masterpieces,* no.120, p.298; *Tales from the Land of Dragons*, no.140, p.228.

[22]*Great Classics: Collections of Ancient Chinese Painting and Calligraphy from the Palace Museum and the Shanghai Museum*, Beijing: Zijincheng Press, 2005, pp.574 - 579.

[23]Anita Chung, *Drawing Boundaries: Architectural Images in Qing China.* Honolulu: University of Hawai'i Press, 2004, p.14.

[24]i.e., Zhao Mengfu (1254 - 1322).

[25]Oubo (Gull Wave) was one of Zhao Mengfu's studio names.

[26]Wu, i.e. the district of Suzhou in Jiangsu province.

[27]Stephen Little with Shawn Eichman, *Taoism and the Arts of China,* Chicago: The Art Institute, 2000, p.159

[28]Roderick Whitfield, *Fascination of Nature: Plants and Insects in Chinese Painting and Ceramics of the Yuan Dynasty (1279 - 1368).* Seoul: Yekyong Publications, 1993, pp.73ff.

[29]A small painting in colours on paper, 26.8 x 45.5cm, showing a melon vine with three melons, with many seals from the Chinese Imperial collection, was shown in 1935 - 36 in the Chinese Exhibition at Burlington House (no.2534). Although labelled as by an anonymous Song artist, the catalogue noted that it was "probably Yuan."

[30]Identified as hairy crabgrass, *Digitaria sanguinalis (L.) Scopoli*, in Toda Teisuke and Ogawa Hiromitsu, *Chugoku no Kachôga,* Tokyo: Gakken Co., 1983, p.153.

[31]*Special Exhibition of Insect Painting,* Taipei: National Palace Museum, 1986, no.4.

[32]Whitfield 1993, *op.cit.*, pp.52 - 53.

[33]*Yanteng* or Yan vine paper, made in Yanxian, now Shengxian, Shaoxing, in Zhejiang Province, has been famed since the Qin and Han dynasties for its smooth white surface.

[34]Whitfield 1993, *op.cit.*, p.54.

[35]See James Cahill, *Hills beyond a River: Chinese Painting of the Yuan Dynasty, 1279 - 1368.* New York and Tokyo, 1976, pl.5.

[36]Only one character is visible, but the seal seems to be the same as that found on *Walking with a Staff over a Bridge,* a square album leaf by the Southern Song artist Bi Liangshi (d. 1150), in the National Palace Museum (*Masterpieces of Chinese Painting in the National Palace Museum,* Supplement, no.12).

[37]See Yang Zhishui. "The Origin and Development of the Lotus Pond Pattern" in Zhao Feng and Shang Gang, eds., 丝绸之路与元代艺术：国际学术讨论会论文集 (*Collected Papers of the International Symposium on the Silk Road and Mongol-Yuan Art*). Hong Kong: ISAT/Costume Squad, 2005, pp. 120 - 31.

[38]*Danqiu ji* 丹丘集 (Collected Writings of Ke Jiusi). Taipei: Xuesheng shudian, 1970, p. 40, poem translated by RW.

Current scholarship in the field of Chinese paintings has not reached a general consensus regarding dating and attribution. Therefore no artists' names or attributions in the catalogue should be taken as unqualified with regard either to authorship or date.

Catalogue

Seven classical Chinese paintings

1

Falconer and Horse

Ink and colour on silk
Attributed to Chen Juzhong (active c. 1201 - 30), Southern Song period
24.8 by 26.3cm

Album leaf of a falconer and horse, the saddled animal caparisoned with a tiger-skin, the falconer wearing a belted robe and tight-fitting cap, with a peregrine falcon perched on his right arm.

Signed: Chen Juzhong hua, perhaps added at a later date.

Stamped with six seals, the first possibly contemporary with the painting, the others added at a later date, the second and third naming specific collectors:

[?] Shoucang shuhua yin.
Jinfu tushu (the seal of Zhu Gang, Prince of Jin, 1358 - 1398)[1].
Liu Quan Jianshang.
Zhenmi.
Xishizhibao.
Yunpu.

出猎图
设色绢本
陈居中（活跃于约公元 1201年 – 1230年） 南宋
纵 24.8公分 横 26.3公分

册页，擎鹰者侍立马旁，伺机出猎，马配虎皮纹鞍。猎人身穿系带长袍，头扎便帽，一只硕大的海冬青立于右前臂。此画用笔简洁，神态跃然。

落款：陈居中画，此款或为后加。
钤印六方：［?］收藏书画印，晋府图书，刘泉鉴赏，珍秘，希世之宝，云浦。

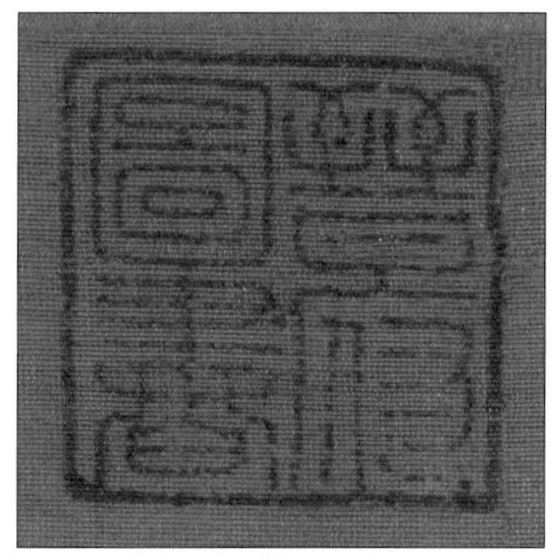

Jinfu tushu

[?] Shoucang shuhua yin

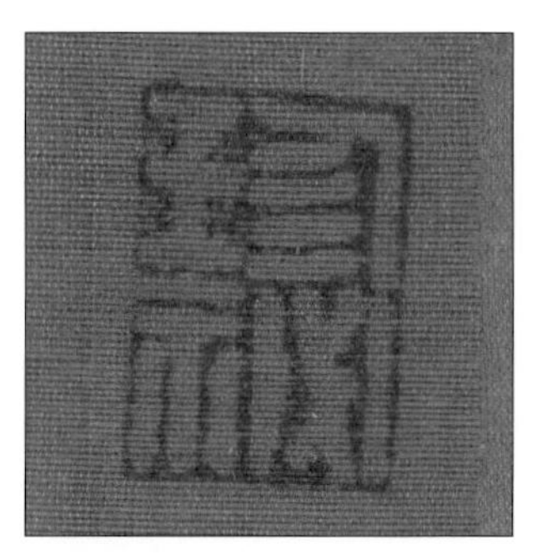

Zhenmi

Xishizhibao

Yunpu

Liu Quan Jianshang

Published:

Sotheby's, New York, *Fine Chinese Paintings*, 13 June 1984, number 1.

Similar examples:

Masterpieces of Chinese Album Painting in the National Palace Museum, Taibei, 1971, number 31, for 'Horse and Groom on a Plain', signed by and attributed to Chen Juzhong.

Robert E. Harrist, Jr., *Power and Virtue, The Horse in Chinese Art*, China Institute, New York, 1997, number 17, pages 84 - 5, for 'Nomad Horsemen Hunting', a fan painting mounted as an album leaf, attributed to Chen Juzhong, in the Metropolitan Museum of Art, New York; and figure 13, page 37, for 'Tartar Horsemen Hunting', also attributed to Chen Juzhong, in the Cleveland Museum of Art.

Jan Fontein and Pratapaditya Pal, *Museum of Fine Arts, Boston, Oriental Art*, Boston, 1969, plate 75, for a detail of one of four album leaves in the museum, of an original series of eighteen illustrating the Han period story of Lady Wenjia's captivity in Mongolia and subsequent return to China. In volume III of *Chinese Painting*, London, 1956, plates 316 - 318, Osvald Sirén captions the illustrations as "Ch'ên Chü-chung [Chen Juzhong], in his manner". They are now attributed by the museum to the Southern Song Dynasty, second quarter of the 12th century.

Wu Tung, *Tales from the Land of Dragons: 1000 Years of Chinese Painting*, Museum of Fine Arts, Boston, 1997, plate 16, page 145, for 'Khitan Falconer with Horse'. Also illustrated as figure 1, page 8, of the present catalogue.

Chen Juzhong served as a court painter or *daizhao* in the Hangzhou Academy during the Jiatai era (1201- 1204); little is known of him otherwise. He specialized in paintings of horses and camp scenes.

In the1997 China Institute catalogue cited above, on page 84, the author states[2] '..the emperor and his party "released eagles and falcons to catch swans and wild geese ... All the imperial attendants donned dark green clothes". The painting in the present exhibition, with its green-garbed falconer, could hardly illustrate this comment more fittingly despite the fact that it refers to the *nabo* or imperial spring hunt of the Liao (Khitan) - who had been overwhelmed in Northern China many decades before Chen Juzhong could have taken his presumed journey north to Shaanxi province. In the late 12th - early 13th century it was the Jin (Jurchen) who ruled there. Nevertheless, Khitan customs may well have been subsumed into those of the Jurchen.

[1]Zhu Gang was an older brother of Zhu Di who would reign as the Yongle emperor, 1403 - 1424.

[2]Referencing Karl A. Wittfogel and Fêng Chia-shêng, *History of Chinese Society: Liao, 907 - 1125*, The American Philosophical Society, Philadelphia, 1949, page 132.

2
Landscape
Ink and colour on silk
Anonymous, Southern Song period, early 13th century
25.0 by 26.6cm

Album leaf of a landscape of distant mountains, hills, trees and grasses with one flock of birds in flight and another, of waterfowl, standing on the bank of a river or lake.

Stamped with two collectors' seals:
Shaoxun[1] and another.

山水图
设色绢本
佚名作　南宋　公元十三世纪早期
纵 25.0公分　横 26.6 公分

风景册页，画中勾勒远岫近岭，平林幽草，又描绘了飞鸟凌空，水禽临湖，笔墨含蓄，意境清寂。

钤印二方：绍勋，字迹不可辩。

Published:

Sotheby's, New York, *Fine Chinese Paintings*, 4 December 1986, number 2.

Similar examples:

Nezu Institute of Fine Arts, *Southern Song Paintings, Elegant and Noble in Soul*, Tokyo, 2004, plates 32 and 33, for two Southern Song album leaves comparable in subject matter.

[1]Shaoxun is one of the names adopted by Shi Miyuan (died 1233), chief minister for many years at the Southern Song court. The identification of Shi Miyuan with Shaoxun (the seal is the double-gourd-shaped one on the present painting) was made a few years ago by Xu Bangda (born 1911), a leading authority on Chinese classical painting at the Palace Museum, Beijing. At least two other paintings – a scroll in the Palace Museum, Beijing[2] and another, painted by the Northern Song emperor, Zhaoji, in the Liaoning Provincial Museum[3] – are stamped with the collector's name Shaoxun in the same seal format. The imprint of the seal alone is illustrated in: Shanghai Museum, *Zhongguo shuhuajia yinjian kuanshi*, (Seals and Signatures of Chinese Painters and Calligraphers), Beijing, 1987, page 218, number 144.

[2]See Liu Jiu'an, *Zhongguo wenwu jinghua dacidian, shu hua juan*, (Comprehensive selection of Chinese cultural objects, painting and calligraphy), Hong Kong, 1996, number 47.

[3]See *Liaoning sheng bowuguan*, (Liaoning Provincial Museum), Beijing, 1983, plates 93 - 4, seal illustrated below:

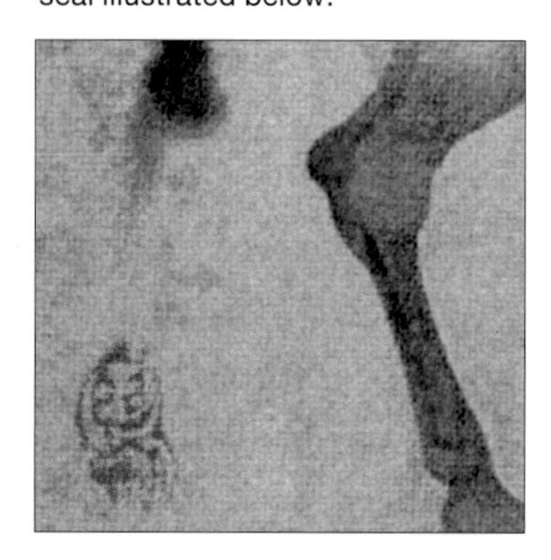

Detail after *Liaoning sheng bowuguan,* Beijing, 1983, plate 93, left hand corner showing Shaoxun seal.

Shaoxun

[?]

3

Girls Gathering Foxnuts

Ink and colour on silk
Anonymous, Yuan period, 13th - 14th century
23.5 by 23.0cm

With a colophon by Fei Danxu (1801-1850)

Album leaf depicting two girls leaning out of opposite sides of a boat, under a willow tree. The girls are harvesting the seeds of the foxnut or gorgon plant (*Euryale ferox*), a member of the water lily family. One girl is shown lifting one of the large, rounded leaves of the plants that float on the surface of the water, amongst sedges.

Stamped with two collectors' seals:

One of Zhang Shouxian (1804 - 1875): Zhangshi Zibo guomu, (*Shanghai*[1], page 916, number 6).
One of the 20th century collector Ma Jizuo: Ma Jizuo yin.

And another, probably apocryphal, of the artist Zhao Mengfu (1254 - 1322):

Zhaoshi Zi'ang (*Shanghai*[1], page 1349, numbers 3 and 4).

采芡图
设色绢本
佚名作　南宋－元　公元十三世纪
纵 23.5 公分　横 23.0 公分

绢本册页，图中两女，烟波泛舟，柳阴垂拂。姑娘们拨开浮萍，繁忙采芡，一片南国水乡秋收景致。

钤印三方：赵孟頫（公元1254年－1322年）：赵氏子昂，（尚待证实）。
章绶衔（公元1804年－1875年）：章氏子柏过目。
马积祚印。

Published:

Christie's, New York, *Important Classical Chinese Paintings*, 31 May 1990, number 8.

Similar example:

Zhongguo huihua quanji, volume 6, Beijing, 1999, plate 103, for a fan-shaped album leaf in the Palace Museum, Beijing, depicting several figures in a boat, amidst lily pads, beneath a willow tree.

Ma Jizuo yin

Zhangshi Zibo guomu

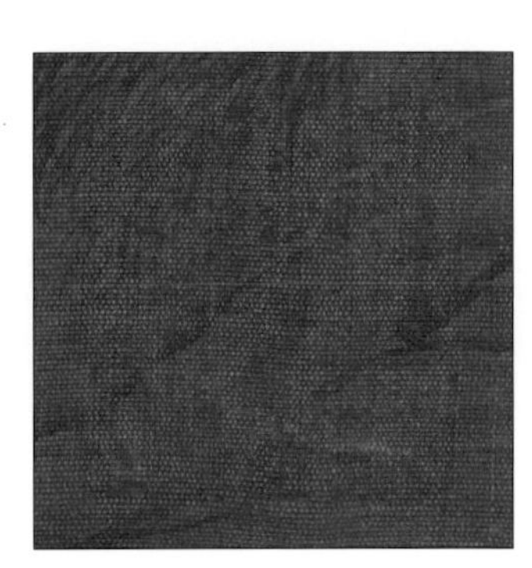
Zhaoshi Zi’ang

Colophon and five seals of Fei Danxu (1801 - 1850), the colophon dated to the twenty-eighth year of Daoguang (corresponding to 1848). For a full translation, see Roderick Whitfield's introduction to this catalogue, page 11. Four of the seals illustrated in *Shanghai*[1], page 1253, numbers 11 and 15 and page 1254, numbers 27 and 28.

费丹旭（1801年 - 1850年）的题跋和钤印五方，此跋题于清道光二十八年(1848年)。其中四方钤印见于上海博物馆出版的（中国书画家印鉴款识):
1253页的11和15，1254页的27和28。

The foxnut blooms and fruits under the water, rather than on or above it. The girl shown lifting up one of the wide, heavy leaves, is searching for the seeds of the plant – believed, in Chinese medicine, to restore youthful vigour and combat impotence. The fact that we see here young, pretty girls reaping this harvest may be a sly allusion to the benefits the ingestion of *qianshi* will bring.

The rivers and lakes of China supported many plants that provided an abundant and varied supply of seeds and corms both for nutritional and medicinal use (sometimes hard to differentiate). Other examples of such aquatic plants are the water caltrop (*Trapa bicornis*), 菱角 *lingjiao* and the water chestnut (*Eleocharis dulcis*) 荸荠 *biqi*.

[1]*Shanghai* refers throughout to Shanghai Museum, *Zhongguo shuhuajia yinjian kuanshi*, (Seals and Signatures of Chinese Painters and Calligraphers), two volumes, Beijing, 1987.

生後先生六百秋披圖重見舊風流鷗波亭外春無
恙尚有吳娃采芡不

文敏書畫冠絕古今旭幸生是鄉流風遺韻薰被良
多戊申冬小住荻溪章子紫伯生所藏採芡冊見貽景
覽名搆悅置身鷗波亭中惜亭址久湮渺渺烟波為往
來舟檝要道居人絕無種芡者故詩中及之雖云託興亦
以絕寶也道光二十有八年長至前三日後學費丹旭謹識

4

An Old Man Resting Under Pine Trees

Ink and colour on silk, mounted on board
Anonymous, Yuan - early Ming period, 14th century
Diameter: 26.8cm

Album leaf mounted on board, now circular, perhaps reduced from a square or rectangular composition. The painting depicts an elderly gentleman holding a staff resting in a landscape, by a riverbank, under tall, gnarled pine trees.

松寿图
设色绢本　册页
佚名作　元－明早期　公元十四世纪
直径：26.8 公分

圆形画面，曾被剪裁。画上松树苍劲，疏密相间，老者倚仗自得，悠然其中。背景波光水色，交映成趣。

Provenance:

Yamanaka & Company, New York.
Stephen Junkunc III, Chicago.

Published:

Christie's, New York, *Fine Chinese Paintings and Calligraphy*, 27 March 1996, number 13.

Similar example:

National Palace Museum, *Masterpieces of Chinese Album Painting in the National Palace Museum*, Taibei, 1971, plate 38, for a fan-shaped album leaf attributed to Sheng Mao, showing a figure in a boat under a tree.

The artist, collector and connoisseur Wang Jiqian (Wang Chi-Ch'ien, C.C. Wang) believed the painting in the present exhibition attributable to 'the hand of Sheng Mao' (1295 - 1368).

5

Pavilion of Prince Teng

Ink on silk
Attributed to Wang Zhenpeng (c. 1280 - c. 1329), or a close follower,
Yuan period, dated 1312
35.9cm by 71.4cm

Handscroll, probably reduced in length, depicting the pavilion or palace of the Tang (7th century) imperial Prince Teng, as evoked by Wang Bo's poem 'Preface to the Pavilion of Prince Teng' written out at the top left corner of the painting. The minutely drawn buildings appear to float in the clouds above the river, a mountainous landscape receding into the distance.

Signed: Guyun chushi (Hermit of the Lonely Cloud) Wang Zhenpeng shuhua.

Dated, before the signature: Huangqing yuannian zhongqiu (first year of Huangqing [1312], mid-autumn), after the transcription of Wang Bo's 'Preface'.

Stamped with three artist's seals: Wang Zhenpeng, Pengmei and Cihao Guyun chushi, the latter in the form of a double-gourd.

滕王阁图
水墨绢本
王振鹏（公元 1280 年 – 1329 年）或弟子代笔。　元　公元 1312 年画
纵 35.9 公分　横 71.4 公分

立轴，长度或短于原作。此画表现了唐代（七世纪）滕王李元婴之别居，把巍峨的楼阁融于云水山光之中，气势宏伟，结构精巧。画幅上左角小楷书写唐代王勃著名的‘滕王阁诗序’全文。

画中自题：孤云处士王振鹏书画。日期于题款前：皇庆元年中秋（公元 1312 年）
钤印三方：王振鹏，朋梅，赐号孤云处士。

Provenance:

According to Berthold Laufer (see below), from the collection of the statesman Li Hongzhang (1823 - 1901).

Published:

Berthold Laufer, *T'ang, Sung and Yuan Paintings Belonging to Various Chinese Collectors*, Paris and Brussels, 1924, plate 27. This is the catalogue of an exhibition of paintings owned by Shanghai collectors, organized by C.T. Loo in 1923; it is perhaps the source of the note by James Cahill, *An Index of Early Chinese Painters and Paintings*, Berkeley, 1980, on page 336.

Sotheby's New York*, Fine Chinese Paintings,* 30 November 1988, number 4.

Similar examples:

Sherman E. Lee and Wai-Kam Ho, *Chinese Art under the Mongols: The Yüan Dynasty (1279 - 1368)*, Cleveland, 1968, number 202, for the handscroll 'Dragon Boat Regatta' now in the Metropolitan Museum of Art, New York.

Yunnan Provincial Museum, *Yunnan sheng bowuguan*, Beijing, 1991, plate 155, for an album leaf depicting the Yellow Crane Pavilion (*Huanghe lou*), on the Yangzi river in Wuhan, Hubei province, by Xia Yong, a close follower of Wang Zhenpeng.

Wu Tung, *Masterpieces of Chinese Painting from the Museum of Fine Arts, Boston: Tang through Yuan Dynasties*,Tokyo, 1996, plate 120, for the album leaf by Xia Yong, 'Palace of Prince Teng'. Also illustrated as figure 2, page 12, of the present catalogue.

Wang Zhenpeng is held to be the foremost Yuan practitioner of a painting style, known as *Jiehua* (boundary painting). Typically, such paintings incorporate architectural scenes or vistas depicted in minute detail, employing a very fine brush and a ruler.

The palace of Prince Teng (Li Yuanying), situated in Nanchang, Jiangxi province, on the Gan river, became renowned throughout China for its architectural beauty. The popularity of Wang Bo's poem 'Preface to the Pavilion of Prince Teng' – apparently composed immediately after the rebuilding or embellishment of Prince Teng's pavilion by his successor as governor of Nanchang – as well as writings by other poets and scholars, contributed largely to its fame. The corner towers of the Forbidden City in Beijing are said to have been inspired by Song period paintings of the Yellow Crane and Prince Teng's pavilions.

The building currently occupying the site of Prince Teng's pavilion, the twenty-eighth since Tang times, was constructed in 1989.

6

Ducks in a Lotus Pond

Ink and colour on silk
Anonymous, Southern Song - Yuan period, 13th century
23.3 by 23.5cm

Fan painting or album leaf mounted as a hanging scroll showing an assembly of ducks swimming in a pond amongst lotus plants and reeds, the leaves of the lotus veined and painted in differing tones of green, three of the full blooms pink, one white.

Stamped with two collectors' seals:

One of Zhu Zixin: Huaiyin Zhu Zixin Zhujingting zhenwan[1].
One of the 20th century collector Ma Jizuo: Ma Jizuo yin.

荷塘鸭乐图
设色绢本
佚名作　南宋－元　公元十三世纪
纵 23.3 公分　横 23.5 公分

立轴式纨扇画面，表现鸭群戏水，莲花粉白，清丽宜人。荷叶赋色典雅，老嫩有别，且寓意吉祥。

钤印二方：淮阴朱子新驻景亭珍玩，马积祚印。

Provenance:

James Freeman, Kyoto.

Exhibited:

New York, Hanart Gallery, 1988.

Published:

Hanart Gallery Inc., *Chinese Paintings & Calligraphy*, New York, November 22 to December 17, 1988, number 3.

Similar example:

Masterpieces of Chinese Album Painting in the National Palace Museum, Taibei, plate 32, 1971, for the famous Southern Song album leaf 'Lotus and Mandarin Ducks', also known as 'Lotus in the Wind', attributed to Feng Dayou. Also illustrated as figure 3, page 15, of the present catalogue. Such a work was probably the inspiration for the painting in this exhibition.

[1]The same seal appears on a hanging scroll in the National Palace Museum, Taibei, depicting five figures walking in an autumn landscape, accession number: painting K2A001783:

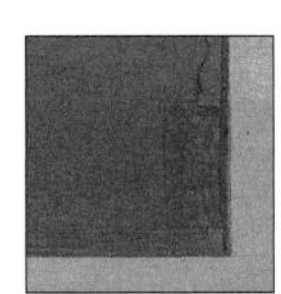

Attributed to Zhao Gan, c. 10th century
Detail showing Shen Zhou Huaiyin Zhu Zixin Zhujingting zhenwan seal in the right hand corner
National Palace Museum, Taibei.

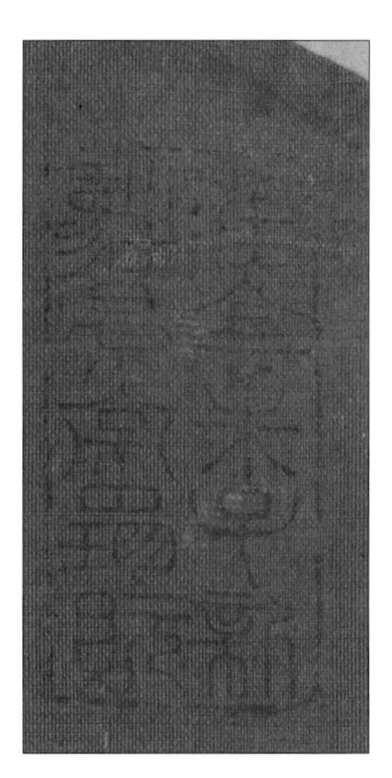

Huaiyin Zhu Zixin Zhujingting zhenwan

Ma Jizuo yin

7
Melon and Grasses
Ink and colour on paper
Anonymous, Yuan - early Ming period, late 14th - early 15th century
27.0 by 28.5cm

Album leaf depicting a melon plant, one large fruit lying on the ground partly hidden by leaves, its flowering, sinuous stem and scrolling tendrils mingling with spiky, feathery grasses.

Stamped with ten collectors' seals:

Six of Xiang Yuanbian (1525 - 1590): Zuili (*C & W*[1], page 610, number 8), Molin miwan (*C & W*, page 611, number 25), Shenyou xinshang (*C & W*, page 611, number 37), Xiang Zijing jia zhencang (*C & W*, page 612, number 63), Tianlaige (*C & W*, page 612, number 65), Xiang Yuanbian yin (*C & W*, page 700, number 71).
One of Shen Zhou (1427 - 1509): Shen Zhou baowan[2].
One of Wu Ting (c. 1600): Wu Ting.
Two (part only) of the Qianlong emperor: Sanxitang (*C & W*, page 583, number 50) and Jixia jianshang zhixi (*C & W*, page 583, number 35).

Three additional 20th century collectors' seals have been cut away (presumably from a previous mount) and fixed to the present mount, two of them of Zhang Xueliang (1901 - 2001)[3]: Yi'an and Zhang Xueliang yin; and one of Feng Hairuo: Feng Hairuo jiancangzhen (see this page below).

瓜草图
设色纸本
佚名作　元－明早期　公元十四世纪 － 公元十五世纪早期
纵 27.0 公分　横 28.5 公分

册页描述了了瓜熟草丰，藤蔓缠绕，花繁叶茂的自然场面。笔精墨妙，生机勃勃。

钤印十方：
六方属项元汴（公元1525年 － 1590年）：**檇**李，墨林秘玩，神游心赏，
项子京家珍藏，天籁阁，项元汴印。
一方属沈周（公元1427年 － 1509年）：沈周宝玩。
一方属吴廷（大约1600年）：吴廷。
两方属乾隆皇帝：三希堂，**幾**暇鉴赏之玺。

另有三方于画外：毅**盦**，张学良印，冯海若鉴藏珍。

Yi'an

Zhang Xueliang yin

Feng Hairuo jiancangzhen

Jixia jianshang zhixi

Sanxitang

Tianlaige

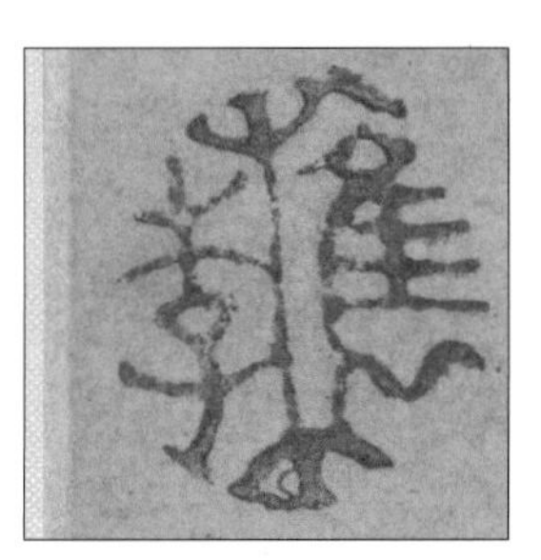

Zuili

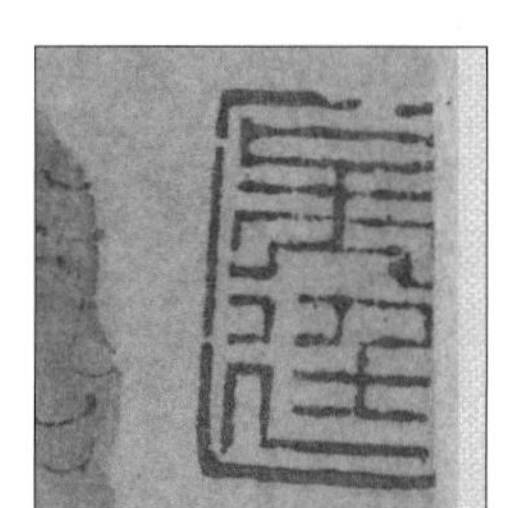

Wu Ting

Shenyou xinshang

Xiang Yuanbian yin

Molin miwan

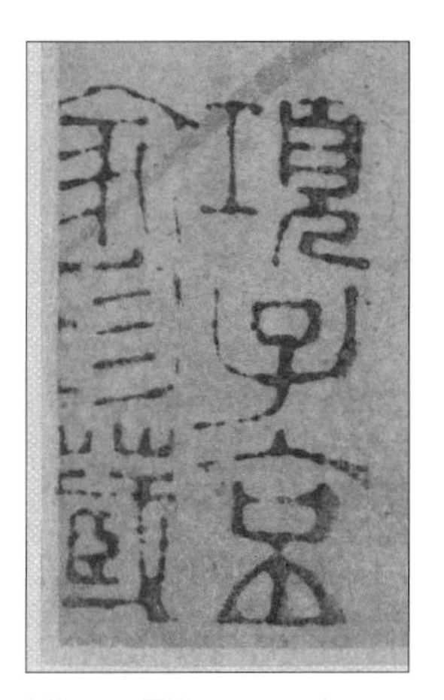

Xiang Zijing jia zhencang

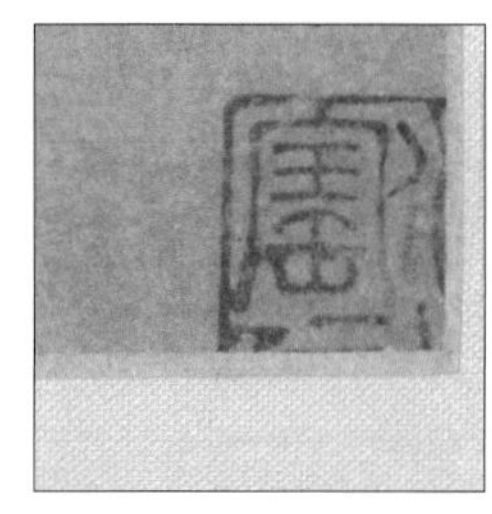

Shen Zhou baowan

Provenance:

Zhang Xueliang, Taiwan.

Published:

Sotheby's, New York, *Fine Chinese Paintings*, 2 June 1987, number 3.

Similar examples:

James Cahill, *Hills Beyond a River*, New York, 1976, plate 5, for a hanging scroll depicting a very similar – although reversed – composition attributed to Qian Xuan (c. 1235 - after 1301).

National Palace Museum, *Famous Album Leaves of the Sung Dynasty*, Taibei, 1995, plate 68, for 'Insect and Pumpkin', an anonymous Song period album leaf; also published National Palace Museum, *China at the Inception of the Second Millennium, Art and Culture of the Sung Dynasty, 960 - 1279*, Taibei, 2000, plate II - 7, page 120.

[1] *C & W* refers throughout to Victoria Contag and Wang Chi-Ch'ien, *Seals of Chinese Painters and Collectors of the Ming and Ch'ing Periods*, Hong Kong, 1966.

[2] The same seal appears on 'Walking with a staff over a bridge', Bi Liangshi, c. 12th century, in the National Palace Museum, Taibei, accession number: painting K2A001247, see detailed image below:

[3] Zhang Xueliang was a charismatic Manchurian 'warlord' and ally of Jiang Jieshi (Chiang Kai-shek) until the 'Xi'an Incident' in December 1936, after which he was kept under house arrest by the Nationalist government for over fifty years – first in mainland China and subsequently in Taiwan.

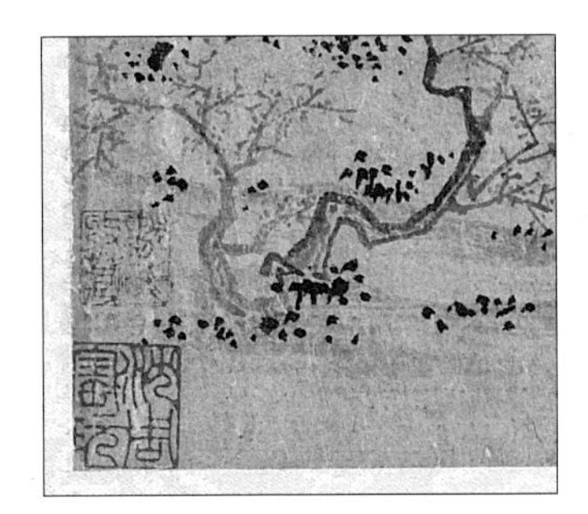

Bi Liangshi, c. 12th century
Detail of *Walking with a Staff over a Bridge,* showing Shen Zhou baowan seal in the left hand corner
National Palace Museum, Taibei.

Bibliography

Archives of the Chinese Art Sociey of America/Archives of Asian Art, New York, 1945 - .

Artibus Asiae, Dresden and Ascona, 1925 - .

Barnhart, R. M.: *Along the Border of Heaven, Sung and Yuan Paintings from the C. C. Wang Family Collection*, The Metropolitan Museum of Art, New York, 1983.

Barnhart, R. M. et al.: *Three Thousand Years of Chinese Painting*, New Haven & London, 1997.

Cahill, J.: *Hills Beyond a River: Chinese Painting of the Yüan Dynasty*, New York, 1976.

Cahill, J.: *Parting at the Shore: Chinese Painting of the Early and Middle Ming Dynasty, 1368 - 1580*, New York, 1978.

Cahill, J.: *An Index of Early Chinese Painters and Paintings*, Berkeley, 1980.

Cleveland Museum of Art, *Eight Dynasties of Chinese Painting: The Collections of the Nelson Gallery-Atkins Museum, Kansas City, and The Cleveland Museum of Art*, Cleveland, 1980.

Cohn, W.: *Chinese Painting*, London, 1948.

Contag, V. and Wang, Chi-Ch'ien: *Seals of Chinese Painters and Collectors of the Ming and Ch'ing Periods*, Hong Kong, 1966.

Cultural Relics Publishing House*, Illustrated Catalogue of Selected Works of Ancient Chinese Painting and Calligraphy*, 24 volumes, Beijing, 1986 - 2008.

Ecke, G.: *Chinese Painting in Hawaii*, 3 volumes, Honolulu, 1965.

Fong, Wen C.: *Summer Mountains: The Timeless Landscape*, New York, 1975.

Fong, Wen C. et al.: *Images of the Mind, Selections from the Edward L. Elliott Family and John B. Elliott Collections of Chinese Calligraphy and Painting at The Art Museum, Princeton University*, Princeton, 1984.

Fong, Wen C. and Watt, James C. Y.: *Possessing the Past, Treasures from the National Palace Museum*, Taipei, Metropolitan Museum of Art, New York, 1996.

Fontein, J. and Pal, P.: *Museum of Fine Arts Boston, Oriental Art*, Boston, 1969.

Fu, Marilyn and Fu, Shen: *Studies in Connoisseurship: Chinese Paintings from the Arthur M. Sackler Collection in New York and Princeton*, Princeton, revised edition, 1976.

Hanart Gallery Inc., *Chinese Paintings & Calligraphy*, New York, 1988.

Harrist Jr., R. E.: *Power and Virtue, The Horse in Chinese Art*, China Institute, New York, 1997.

Hearn, Maxwell K. and Smith, Judith G. eds.: *Arts of the Sung and Yüan, symposium papers published in conjunction with Possessing the Past*, Metropolitan Museum, New York, 1996.

Hearn, M. K.: *How to Read Chinese Paintings*, The Metropolitan Museum of Art, New York, 2008.

Laufer, B.: *T'ang, Sung and Yüan Paintings Belonging to Various Chinese Collectors*, Paris and Brussels, 1924.

Lawton, T.: *Chinese Figure Painting, Freer Gallery of Art Fiftieth Anniversary Exhibition II*, Washington, 1973.

Lee, Hui-shu: *Exquisite Moments: West Lake & Southern Song Art*, China Institute, New York, 2001.

Ledderose, L.: *Orchiden und Felsen, Chinesische Bilder im Museum für Ostasiatische Kunst, Berlin*, Berlin, 1998.

Lee, S. E. and Ho, Wai-Kam: *Chinese Art under the Mongols: The Yüan Dynasty (1279 - 1368)*, Cleveland, 1968.

Liaoning sheng bowuguan, (Liaoning Provincial Museum), Beijing, 1983.

Liu, Jiu'an ed.: *Zhongguo wenwu jinghua dacidian, Shuhuajuan*, (Comprehensive selection of Chinese cultural objects, painting and calligraphy), Hong Kong, 1996.

Loehr, M.: *The Great Painters of China*, Oxford, 1980.

National Palace Museum, *Masterpieces of Chinese Album Painting in the National Palace Museum*, Taibei, 1971.

National Palace Museum, *Masterpieces of Chinese Painting in the National Palace Museum, Supplement*, Taibei, 1973.

National Palace Museum, *The Four Great Masters of the Yuan*, Taibei, 1975.

National Palace Museum, *Famous Album Leaves of the Sung Dynasty [Special Exhibition]*, Taibei, 1995.

National Palace Museum, *China at the Inception of the Second Millennium, Art and Culture of the Sung Dynasty, 960 - 1279*, Taibei, 2000.

Nezu Institute of Fine Arts, *Southern Song Paintings: Elegant and Noble in Soul*, Tokyo, 2004.

Shanghai Museum, *Zhongguo shuhuajia yinjian kuanshi*, (Seals and Signatures of Chinese Painters and Calligraphers), 2 volumes, Beijing, 1987, reprinted 2007.

Sickman, L. ed.: *Chinese Calligraphy and Painting in the Collection of John M. Crawford, Jr.*, exhibition catalogue, New York, 1962.

Sirén, O.: *A History of Early Chinese Painting*, 2 volumes, London, 1933.

Sirén, O.: *Chinese Painting*, 7 volumes, London, 1956 - 8.

Stanley-Baker, J.: *Old Masters Repainted*, Hong Kong, 1995.

Suzuki, K. ed.: *Comprehensive Illustrated Catalog of Chinese Paintings*, 5 volumes, Tokyo, 1982 - 83.

Wang, C. C.: *Album Leaves from the Sung and Yuan Dynasties*, China Institute, New York, 1970.

Whitfield, R.: *In Pursuit of Antiquity, Chinese Paintings of the Ming and Ch'ing Dynasties from the Collection of Mr. and Mrs. Earl Morse*, Princeton, 1969.

Whitfield, R.: *Fascination of Nature, Plants and Insects in Chinese Painting and Ceramics of the Yuan Dynasty (1279 - 1368)*, Seoul, 1993.

Wittfogel, K. A. and Fêng, Chia-shêng: *History of Chinese Society: Liao, 907 -1125*, The American Philosophical Society, Philadelphia, 1949.

Yonezawa, Y. and Kawakita, M.: *Arts of China, Paintings in Chinese Museums: New Collections*, Tokyo, 1970.

Yunnan sheng bowuguan, (Yunnan Provincial Museum), Beijing, 1991.

Zhongguo huihua quanji, (Comprehensive collection of Chinese paintings), 30 volumes, Beijing, 1997 - 2001.

Works of art purchased from the Eskenazi Galleries, London, are now in the following museum collections:

Ackland Art Museum, North Carolina
Arita Porcelain Park Museum, Saga
Art Gallery of New South Wales, Sydney
Art Gallery of South Australia, Adelaide
Art Institute of Chicago, Chicago
Arthur M. Sackler Gallery, Washington, DC
Art Museum, Princeton University, Princeton
Ashmolean Museum, Oxford
Asia House, Mr and Mrs John D Rockefeller 3rd Collection, New York
Asian Art Museum of San Francisco, San Francisco
Asian Civilisations Museum, Singapore
Baltimore Museum of Art, Baltimore
Birmingham Museum of Art, Alabama
British Museum, London
Brooklyn Museum, New York
Chang Foundation, Taibei
Chung Young Yang Embroidery Museum, Sookmyung Women's University, Seoul, Korea
Cincinnati Art Museum, Cincinnati
Cleveland Museum of Art, Cleveland
Columbus Museum of Art, Columbus
Corning Museum of Glass, Corning
Dallas Museum of Fine Arts, Dallas
Dayton Art Institute, Dayton
Denver Art Museum, Denver
Didrichsen Art Museum, Helsinki
Fitzwilliam Museum, Cambridge
Flagstaff House Museum of Teaware, Hong Kong
Freer Gallery of Art, Washington, DC
Fuji Art Museum, Tokyo
Hagi Uragami Museum, Hagi
Hakone Museum of Art, Hakone
Harvard University Art Museums, Cambridge, Massachusetts
Hetjens Museum, Düsseldorf
Hong Kong Museum of Art, Hong Kong
Honolulu Academy of Arts, Honolulu
Idemitsu Museum of Arts, Tokyo
Indianapolis Museum of Art, Indianapolis
Israel Museum, Jerusalem
Istituto Italiano per il Medio ed Estremo Oriente, Rome
Kimbell Art Museum, Fort Worth
Kuboso Memorial Museum, Izumi City, Osaka
Los Angeles County Museum, Los Angeles
Matsuoka Museum of Art, Tokyo
Metropolitan Museum of Art, New York
Miho Museum, Shigaraki
Minneapolis Institute of Arts, Minneapolis
MOA Museum of Art, Atami
Musée Ariana, Geneva
Musée des Arts Asiatiques, Nice
Musée Guimet, Paris
Musées Royaux d'Art et d'Histoire, Brussels
Museum für Kunst und Gewerbe, Hamburg
Museum für Lackkunst, Münster
Museum für Ostasiatische Kunst, Berlin
Museum für Ostasiatische Kunst, Cologne
Museum of Decorative Art, Copenhagen
Museum of Fine Arts, Boston
Museum of Fine Arts, Houston
Museum of Islamic Art, Doha
Museum of Oriental Ceramics, Osaka
Museum Rietberg, Zurich
National Gallery of Australia, Canberra
National Gallery of Canada, Ottawa
National Gallery of Victoria, Melbourne
National Museum, Singapore
National Museum, Tokyo
Nelson-Atkins Museum of Art, Kansas City
Nezu Institute of Fine Arts, Tokyo
Norton Simon Museum of Art at Pasadena, Pasadena
Östasiatiska Museet, Stockholm
Royal Ontario Museum, Toronto
St. Louis Art Museum, St. Louis
Seattle Art Museum, Seattle
Shanghai Museum, Shanghai
Speed Art Museum, Louisville
Toguri Museum of Art, Tokyo
Tsui Museum of Art, Hong Kong
Victoria & Albert Museum, London
Virginia Museum of Fine Arts, Richmond
Worcester Art Museum, Worcester

Previous Exhibitions

March	1972	Inaugural exhibition Early Chinese ceramics and works of art.
July	1972	Georges Rouault, an exhibition arranged by Richard Nathanson.
June	1973	Ancient Chinese bronze vessels, gilt bronzes and early ceramics.
November	1973	Chinese ceramics from the Cottle collection.
December	1973	Japanese netsuke formerly in the collection of Dr Robert L Greene.
June	1974	Early Chinese ceramics and works of art.
November	1974	Japanese inrō from the collection of E A Wrangham.
May	1975	Japanese netsuke and inrō from private collections.
June	1975	Ancient Chinese bronzes from the Stoclet and Wessén collections.
June	1976	Chinese jades from a private collection.
June	1976	Michael Birch netsuke and sculpture.
June	1976	Japanese netsuke and inrō from private collections.
June	1977	Ancient Chinese bronze vessels, gilt bronzes and sculptures; two private collections, one formerly part of the Minkenhof collection.
June	1978	Ancient Chinese sculpture.
June	1978	Michael Webb netsuke.
June	1978	Eighteenth to twentieth century netsuke.
June	1979	Japanese netsuke from private collections.
June	1980	Japanese netsuke from private collections and Michael Webb netsuke.
July	1980	Ancient Chinese bronzes and gilt bronzes from the Wessén and other collections.
December	1980	Chinese works of art from the collection of J M A J Dawson.
October	1981	Japanese netsuke and inrō from the collection of Professor and Mrs John Hull Grundy and other private collections.
December	1981	Ancient Chinese sculpture.
October	1982	Japanese inrō from private collections.
October	1983	Michael Webb, an English carver of netsuke.
October	1984	Japanese netsuke, ojime, inrō and lacquer-ware.
June	1985	Ancient Chinese bronze vessels, gilt bronzes, inlaid bronzes, silver, jades, ceramics – Twenty five years.
December	1986	Japanese netsuke, ojime, inrō and lacquer-ware.
June	1987	Tang.
June	1989	Chinese and Korean art from the collections of Dr Franco Vannotti, Hans Popper and others.
November	1989	Japanese lacquer-ware from the Verbrugge collection.
December	1989	Chinese art from the Reach family collection.
May	1990	Japanese netsuke from the Lazarnick collection.
June	1990	Ancient Chinese sculpture from the Alsdorf collection and others.
November	1990	The Charles A Greenfield collection of Japanese lacquer.
June	1991	Inlaid bronze and related material from pre-Tang China.
November	1992	Japanese lacquer-ware – recent acquisitions.

December	1992	Chinese lacquer from the Jean-Pierre Dubosc collection and others.
June	1993	Early Chinese art from tombs and temples.
June	1993	Japanese netsuke from the Carré collection.
June	1994	Yuan and early Ming blue and white porcelain.
June	1995	Early Chinese art: 8th century BC-9th century AD.
October	1995	Adornment for Eternity, loan exhibition from the Denver Art Museum.
June	1996	Sculpture and ornament in early Chinese art.
November	1996	Japanese inrō and lacquer-ware from a private Swedish collection.
March	1997	Ceramic sculpture from Han and Tang China.
June	1997	Chinese Buddhist sculpture.
June	1997	Japanese netsuke, ojime and inrō from the Dawson collection.
November	1997	Japanese netsuke – recent acquisitions.
March	1998	Animals and animal designs in Chinese art.
June	1998	Japanese netsuke, ojime and inrō from a private European collection.
November	1998	Chinese works of art and furniture.
March	1999	Ancient Chinese bronzes and ceramics.
November	1999	Ancient Chinese bronzes from an English private collection.
March	2000	Masterpieces from ancient China.
November	2000	Chinese furniture of the 17th and 18th centuries.
March	2001	Tang ceramic sculpture.
November	2001	Chinese ceramic vessels 500 - 1000 AD.
March	2002	Chinese Buddhist sculpture from Northern Wei to Ming.
November	2002	Two rare Chinese porcelain fish jars of the 14th and 16th centuries.
March	2003	Chinese works of art from the Stoclet collection.
November	2003	Song: Chinese ceramics, 10th to 13th century.
March	2004	Chinese Buddhist figures.
November	2004	A selection of Ming and Qing ceramics.
March	2005	Ancient Chinese bronzes and sculpture.
November	2005	Song ceramics from the Hans Popper collection.
March	2006	A selection of early Chinese bronzes.
June	2006	Recent paintings by Arnold Chang.
March	2007	Song: Chinese ceramics, 10th to 13th century *(part 3)*.
November	2007	Mountain landscapes by Li Huayi.
March	2008	Chinese sculpture and works of art.
October	2008	Chinese ceramics and stone sculpture.